Maths for the More Able – A Challenge a Week

YEAR 6

Mary Pardoe

Introduction

This series of six photocopiable books provides additional challenge for more able children. The materials enable you to meet the needs of able mathematicians without developing completely separate topics.

For users of the NNS

Maths For the More Able can be integrated easily into whatever maths material you use if you are following the NNS. The contents list on the inside front cover gives the appropriate reference to the NNS pages. The book contains stimulating challenges to enhance the range of children's mathematical experience.

You can use this book to:
- provide alternative, and more demanding, tasks for more able children during the group work phase of the daily maths lesson;
- provide more challenging homework tasks for the more able mathematicians in your class;
- broaden the range of mathematical experience for a range of children.

Many of the tasks in this book are of an investigative or puzzle-solving variety. In addition to mathematical knowledge, some logical thinking will often be required. The children should enjoy the level of challenge the activities provide, and also the opportunity to choose their own ways of working. This is fundamental to development in mathematics, and you should therefore allow children to decide what aids they will use to help them solve the problems. More able children are often comfortable with abstract tasks, but most of them will at some stage want to use practical apparatus, and this should be allowed.

For users of the Folens Maths Programme

The teacher's pages are correlated to specific lessons in the FMP. You can therefore substitute for your able pupils the activity in this book for the one indicated for that day in the FMP.

The pupil sheets

Photocopiable activity sheets (**AS**) for the children to work on are provided for the lessons and can be used to support group work. For some lessons a photocopiable resource sheet (**RS**) is also provided. It is assumed that all the children will take part in the whole-class introduction to the lesson before tackling the task from this book. Note that Week 7 in each term is set aside for assessment and review.

The teacher notes will guide you in introducing the tasks to the children and in effective ways of working, as well as providing the solutions. These notes will help you to support children appropriately as they work.

Place value, ordering and rounding

Learning objectives

- ◆ Compare and order numbers.
- ◆ Multiply a whole number by 10, 100 and 1000.
- ◆ Explain methods and reasoning about numbers.

Resources

AS 'Greatest product'

Teacher's notes

In this activity pupils are asked to find the greatest product of three, four and five digits using multiplication and diagrams.

The **greatest product** of numbers made using the digits, 1, 2, 3 is 3 x 21 = **63**.

The following system could be tried with the digits 1, 2, 3, 4.
    Four one-digit numbers: 1 x 2 x 3 x 4 = 24
    Two one-digit numbers and one two-digit number; the greatest is 4 x 3 x 21 = 252
    One one-digit number and one three-digit number; the greatest is 4 x 321 = 1284
    Two two-digit numbers; the greatest is 41 x 32 = 1312
The **greatest product** of numbers made using the digits, 1, 2, 3, 4 is 41 x 32 = **1312**.

In this task pupils use the diagram to work out that 52 x 43 is greater than 53 x 42.
The diagram shows the rectangle for 53 x 42 as the sum of the rectangles 52 x 42 and 1 x 42 and it shows the rectangle for 52 x 43 as the sum of the rectangles 52 x 42 and 1 x 52.
It can be seen that **the rectangle for 52 x 43 is bigger than that for 53 x 42**.

This diagram shows that **54 x 63 is greater than 53 x 64**.

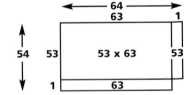

Pupils could try the following system, similar to the one above, with the digits 1, 2, 3, 4, 5.
    Five one-digit numbers: 1 x 2 x 3 x 4 x 5 = 120
    Three one-digit numbers and one two-digits number; the greatest is 5 x 4 x 3 x 21 = 1260
    Two one-digit numbers and one three-digit number; the greatest is 5 x 4 x 321 = 6420
    One one-digit number and two two-digit numbers; the greatest is 5 x 42 x 31 = 6510
    One two-digit number and one three-digit number; the greatest is 52 x 431 = 22 412
    One one-digit number and one four-digit numbers; the greatest is 5 x 4321 = 21 605

Pupils who have reflected on their findings so far should not need to work out all the possibilities. For example, this diagram shows that 431 x 52 is greater than 421 x 53.

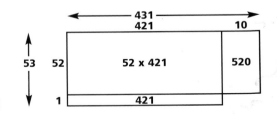

The **greatest product** of the numbers made using the digits, 1, 2, 3, 4, 5 is 52 x 431 = **22 412**.

Greatest product

- Use the digits 1, 2, 3 exactly once each to make two or more numbers, for example 2 and 13.
  Multiply these numbers together, for example 2 x 13 = 26.

  Try other arrangements of the digits 1, 2, 3.
  What is the **greatest product** that can be made?

- Solve the same problem with the digits 1, 2, 3, 4.

- Which is greater: 53 x 42 or 52 x 43?
  Explain how this diagram shows the answer to the question above?

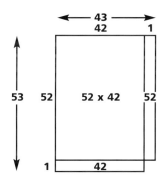

- Which is greater: 54 x 63 or 53 x 64?
  Draw a diagram that shows the answer.

- Use the digits 1, 2, 3, 4, 5 once each to make two or more numbers, for example 4, 21, 53.
  Multiply these numbers together, for example 4 x 21 x 53 = 4452.

  Try other arrangements of the digits 1, 2, 3, 4, 5.
  What is the **greatest product** that can be made?

Write up your findings.

- If you have time you could investigate the greatest products for the digits 1 to 6, 1 to 7 and so on.

Multiplication and division

Learning objectives

◆ Use written methods to find the quotient of two numbers.
◆ Develop written methods for dividing numbers involving decimals.
◆ Select an appropriate division method to find an answer.
◆ Explain methods and reasoning about numbers.
◆ Recognise and explain patterns and relationships, generalise and predict.
◆ Make and investigate a general statement about familiar numbers by finding examples that satisfy it.

Resources

AS 'Repeat numbers'

Teacher's notes

Any six-digit 'repeat' number, **abcabc** is 1001 x **abc**. For example, 237237 = 1001 x 237. Because 7 x 11 x 13 = 1001, dividing first by 7, then by 11 and then by 13 has the same effect as dividing by 1001. This is why the original three-digit number is always obtained. Thus, in the example given on the **AS**:

$$237237 \div 7 = 33891$$
$$33891 \div 11 = 3081$$
$$3081 \div 13 = 237$$

Pupils will get plenty of practice with long division. However, the explanation is the important part for these pupils. The aim is to get them thinking why the final answer has to be the original three-digit number.

Having arrived at a generalisation by trying examples, the real mathematical demand is to understand and to write, in their own words, a proof of that generalisation.

Repeat numbers

- Write a three-digit number, for example 237.
  Repeat it to make a six-digit 'repeat' number, 237237.

Divide the repeat number by 7:	$237237 \div 7$	=	(**first answer**).
Now divide the first answer by 11:	(**first answer**) $\div$ 11	=	(**second answer**).
Now divide the second answer by 13:	(**second answer**) $\div$ 13	=	(**final answer**).

  What happens?

- Start with a different six-digit repeat number and again divide first by 7, then by 11 and then by 13.

  What happens?

- Investigate several other six-digit repeat numbers.

Finding an explanation
Now that you have seen what happens, can you be sure that the same thing will always happen?

Think about what you were dividing by each time and what these numbers have to do with the repeat number and one other special number.

- Try to write an explanation of why the same thing will always happen. Your explanation should be clear enough for anyone to understand.

$237237 \div 7$

Using a calculator

Learning objectives

- ◆ Use a calculator to find a square root.
- ◆ Read a calculator display to two decimal places.
- ◆ Explain methods and reasoning about numbers.

Resources

AS 'Nearer to the root'
Calculators

Teacher's notes

Pupils have to use calculators in this activity to find the square roots of different numbers and discover when the statements are generally false.

Solutions

1. **True.** $\sqrt{60} = 7.746$ (to 3 d.p.), which is nearer to 8 than to 7.
2. **True.** $\sqrt{7.8} = 2.793$ (to 3 d.p.), which is nearer to 3 than to 2.
3. **False.** $\sqrt{2.3} = 1.517$ (to 3 d.p.), which is nearer to 2 than to 1.
4. **False.** $\sqrt{2.25} = 1.5$, which is midway between 1 and 2.
5. **True.** $\sqrt{3} = 1.732$ (to 3 d.p.), which is nearer to 2 than to 1.

Generalisation

For numbers between any two numbers x and y (for example, when x = 0, y = 1), there is a small range between the square of the number midway between $\sqrt{x}$ and $\sqrt{y}$ (when x = 0, y = 1, $\sqrt{0} = 0$ and $\sqrt{1} = 1$, this number is 0.5 x 0.5 = 0.25) and the number midway between x and y (when x = 0, y = 1, this is 0.5) for which the statement is false.

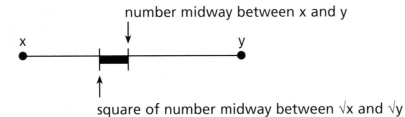

number midway between x and y

square of number midway between $\sqrt{x}$ and $\sqrt{y}$

Nearer to the root

You might expect that because 60 is nearer to 64 than to 49, then √60 would be nearer to the √64 than √49. But is this really the case?

● Are these statements true or false? Use your calculator, then circle your answer.

1. Because 60 is nearer to 64 than to 49, √60 is nearer to 8 than to 7.
True/False

2. Because 7.8 is nearer to 9 than to 4, √7.8 is nearer to 3 than to 2.
True/False

3. Because 2.3 is nearer to 1 than to 4, √2.3 is nearer to 1 than to 2.
True/False

4. Because 2.25 is nearer to 1 than to 4, √2.25 is nearer to 1 than to 2.
True/False

5. Because 3 is nearer to 4 than to 1, √3 is nearer to 2 than to 1.
True/False

● Test similar statements for numbers and their square roots.

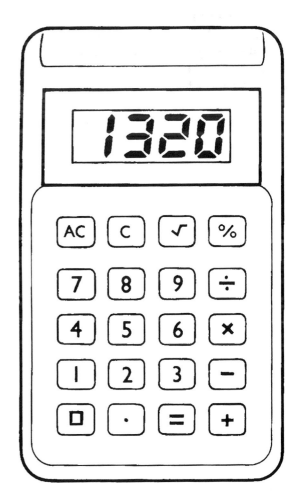

Challenge
Try to find an explanation for your results.

Fractions and decimals

Learning objectives

◆ Find fractions of an amount and of a quantity.
◆ Develop calculator skills and use a calculator effectively.

Resources

AS 'Freddie Frog'
Calculators

Teacher's notes

These problems give plenty of practice in finding fractions of distances. However, they also involve the concepts of infinity and of approaching limits. Incidentally, they also give an opportunity for pupils to think how they can use their calculators efficiently to do the arithmetic.

Number of try	Distance from the bottom of the well* Freddie jumps to:	Distance from the bottom of the well* Freddie slips back to:
1	30m	15m
2	37.5m	18.75m
3	39.375m	19.6875m
4	39.8438m	19.9219m
5	39.961m	19.9805m
6	39.9903m	19.9951m
7	39.9988m	19.9988m
11	39.99999...m	19.99999...m

(*Using a calculator that gives numbers correct to 4 d.p.)

Freddie will never get out. If he goes on for ever, he will get nearer and nearer to 40m (two thirds of the distance up the well), but slip back nearer and nearer to 20m (one third of the distance up the well).

When Freddie tries again **he will still never get out**. If he goes on for ever, he will get nearer and nearer to 48m (four fifths of the distance up the well), but slip back nearer and nearer to 12m (one fifth of the distance up the well).

Freddie Frog

Use a calculator.
Try to use it efficiently.

Freddie Frog is at the bottom of a well. The well is 60 metres deep. He is trying to jump out.

At his first try he jumps $\frac{1}{2}$ way up the well, then slips back $\frac{1}{2}$ the distance between where he reached and the bottom of the well.

At his second try he jumps $\frac{1}{2}$ the distance from where he is to the top, then he slips back $\frac{1}{2}$ the distance to the bottom.

At his third try he jumps $\frac{1}{2}$ the distance from where he is to the top, then slips back $\frac{1}{2}$ the distance to the bottom.

He continues like this, always jumping $\frac{1}{2}$ the distance from where he is to the top, then slipping back $\frac{1}{2}$ the distance from where he reached to the bottom.

● Will Freddie ever get out?
   If not, what is the furthest he will ever get up the well?
   What fraction of the whole distance is this?

● Suppose Freddie changes his method. He starts again from the bottom. This time, at each try, he jumps $\frac{3}{4}$ of the distance from where he is to the top, and then slips back $\frac{3}{4}$ of the distance from where he reached to the bottom. What will happen this time?

Ratio and proportion

Learning objectives

- Respond to written problems involving ratio and proportion.
- Consolidate use of related vocabulary.

Resources

AS 'In gear (1)'
AS 'In gear (2)'

Teacher's notes

In solving these problems, pupils have to interpret the concept of ratio in a practical context. You should look for clear descriptions and diagrams.

For **AS** 'In gear (1)', the solutions are:

1. Gear ratio = $\frac{1}{4}$; B makes **4 complete turns anti-clockwise**.

2. Gear ratio = $\frac{3}{4}$; B makes **$1\frac{1}{3}$ turns anti-clockwise**.

3. Gear ratio = $\frac{3}{2}$; B makes $\frac{2}{3}$ of a complete **turn anti-clockwise**.

4. Gear ratio = 1; B makes **1 complete turn clockwise**.

5. Gear ratio = $\frac{1}{3}$; B makes **3 complete turns clockwise**.

6. Gear ratio = $\frac{3}{5}$; B makes **$1\frac{2}{3}$ turns clockwise**.

For **AS** 'In gear (2)', check pupils' own diagrams for questions 1–6 and question 8.

7. The numbers of teeth of wheels A, B, and C can be any multiple of 9, 6 and 4 that is greater than 2. For example, A: 27, B: 18, C: 12 or A: 36, B: 24, C:16 and so on.

In gear (1)

Each time gear wheel A makes exactly one turn clockwise, gear wheel B makes exactly three whole turns anti-clockwise. The gear ratio of B to A is $\frac{1}{3}$.

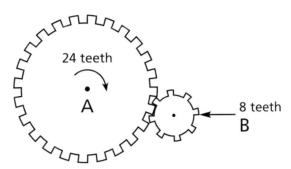

● For each gear system state the gear ratio and describe what happens to B each time A makes exactly one turn clockwise.

1.

2.

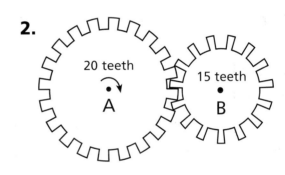

3.

4.

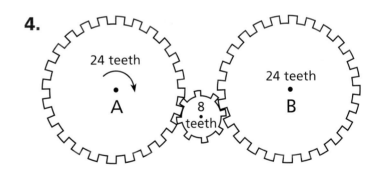

5.

6.

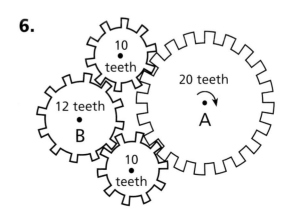

In gear (2)

- Design and sketch your own gear systems with the gear ratios given below. In each system give gear wheel A at least 10 teeth.

   1. $\frac{2}{3}$

   2. $\frac{5}{8}$

   3. $\frac{3}{4}$

   4. $2\frac{1}{2}$

   5. $\frac{4}{3}$

   6. $1\frac{2}{5}$

7. In this three-gear system the gear ratio of B to A is $\frac{2}{3}$ and the gear ratio of C to B is also $\frac{2}{3}$.

   Gear wheel A has at least 20 teeth. How many teeth could each wheel have? Find a least two possible answers.

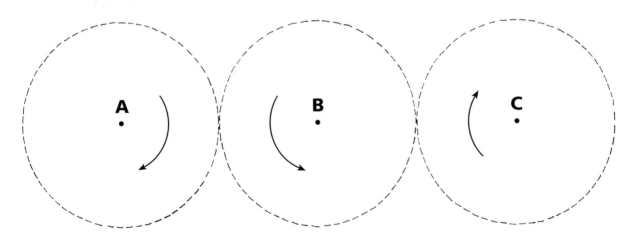

8. Design three-gear systems with each of these gear ratios.

   a. B to A = $\frac{1}{2}$, C to B = $\frac{1}{3}$

   b. B to A = $\frac{4}{3}$, C to B = $1\frac{1}{2}$

 Maths for the More Able 6

FOLENS MATHS PROGRAMME

- One Teacher File for each term, for each year group.

- Each File contains a lesson plan for every lesson in the term.

- All lesson plans include the introductory session, the main focus (for whole class, group and independent activities) and the plenary focus.

- Photocopiable pupil activity sheets are provided.

- Lesson plans contain differentiated activities for three levels of ability.

Author Team

The six principal writers are all practising teachers who have trialled the NNP and, therefore, have significant experience of the Framework.

- The team co-ordinator is Jill Clare, Adviser for Thurrock.

- The specialist Maths consultant is Barbara Allebone, Goldsmiths' College, Lecturer in Primary Maths.

- The publisher is Dr. Steve Sizmur, previously responsible for Primary SAT developments at NFER.

DAILY LESSON PLANS

- The introductory 10 minutes mental calculation work

- The main activity for the whole class and for groups of differing ability

- The plenary session with the whole class

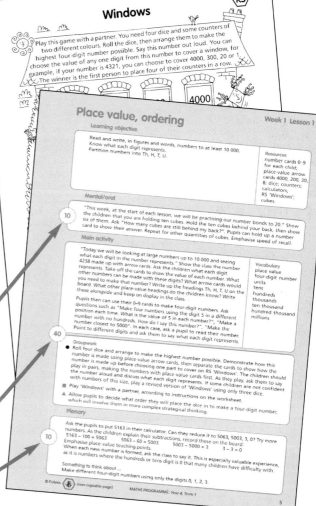

▼ PHOTOCOPIABLE ORDER FORM ▼

Handling data

Learning objectives

- ◆ Read from a line graph.
- ◆ Represent data in a line graph.
- ◆ Interrogate data from own line graph.

Resources

AS 'Juice tanks'

Teacher's notes

This activity should help pupils understand that a graph with a constantly changing gradient is a curve. In solving the problems pupils really have to think about what the gradient of a graph represents. In this context, the rate at which the height of liquid in a tank increases as the volume increases.

The last task requires at least two pupils to work together.

Solutions

1.

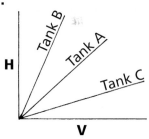

2.

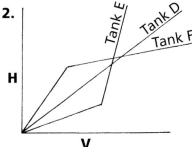

3.

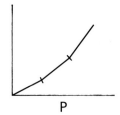

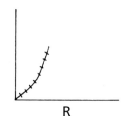

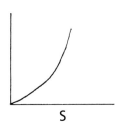

4. Tank X: graph 2
Tank Y: graph 4
Tank Z: graph 1

A possible tank shape for graph 3.

Juice tanks

At Job's juice factory the juice tanks are different shapes.

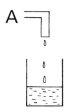  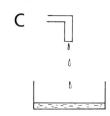 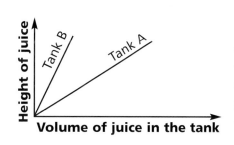

The graph shows how the height of the juice in tanks A and B varies as juice drips steadily into them.

1. Copy the graphs and, on the same diagram, sketch a graph for tank C.

2. Copy the graph for tank D and, on the same diagram, sketch graphs for tanks E and F.

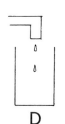 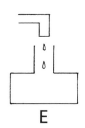  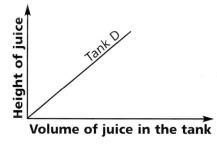

3. Sketch graphs for the following tanks.

   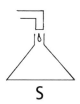

Use your sketches to explain why a tank with straight sloping sides (like tank S) does not give a straight-line graph.

4. Here are three tanks and four graphs.
Choose the correct graph for each tank. Explain why it is the correct graph. For the remaining graph, sketch what the tank should look like.

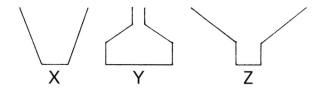 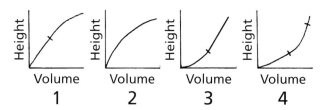

5. Invent your own tank shapes. On a different sheet of paper sketch the graph for each tank. Pass your sketches to someone in your class to see if they can draw the shapes of your tanks from the graphs.

Calculator skills and checking results

Learning objectives

- ◆ Use trial and improvement method to solve a problem.
- ◆ Use related vocabulary.
- ◆ Use a calculator correctly.

Resources

AS 'Same number puzzles'
Calculators

Teacher's notes

Pupils should read carefully through the example before trying the three puzzles.

It is important that pupils keep a record of their trials, as in the example. They should, thereby, show that they have used trial and improvement, as opposed to trial and error, to work towards the solutions.

Pupils should understand the crucial difference between 'trial and improvement' and 'trial and error' methods. 'Trial and error' means you rule out possible solutions by trying them at random and finding they do not work. When using 'trial and improvement' you use the result of each trial to guide you closer to the solution.

Solutions
1. 4.14
2. 6.141
3. 33.16

Same number puzzles

Example:
Find one number that will go in each △ to make the equation true.

(It must be the same number in each △.)

$$\triangle + (\triangle \times \triangle) = 17$$

There is no whole number solution. 4 + (4 x 4) = 20 is too big!
3 + (3 x 3) = 12 is too small!

One pupil used trial and improvement to try to get nearer to 17. She kept a record of her trials. After each try she used the result to improve on her last try.

Try	Result	
3.5	15.75	too small
3.6	16.56	too small
3.7	17.39	too big
3.65	16.9725	too small
3.66	17.0556	too big
3.655	17.014	too big
3.654	17.0057	too big
3.653	16.9974	too small

I'll try the number midway between 3.6 and 3.7.

Both 3.654 and 3.653 give results very close to 17, but one is too big and the other is too small, but 3.653 gives a result closer to 17 than 3.654 (17.0057 − 17 = 0.0057, 17 − 16.9974 = 0.0026).
So 3.653 is the solution to 3 decimal places (to 3 d.p.).

● Use trial and improvement to find solutions to these puzzles.
Use a calculator.
In each puzzle the same number goes in each △.
Keep a record of your trials.

1. $\triangle \times (\triangle - 1) = 13$ (Find solution to 2 d.p.)

2. $(\triangle \times \triangle) + (2 \times \triangle) = 50$ (Find solution to 3 d.p.)

3. $(\triangle \times \triangle) - (3 \times \triangle) = 1000$ (Find solution to 2 d.p.)

Properties of 3-D and 2-D shapes

Learning objectives

- ◆ Recognise that a net can be used to make a cube.
- ◆ Know that a variety of nets will make a closed cube.
- ◆ Successfully construct nets for a closed cube.
- ◆ Solve mathematical problems or puzzles.

Resources

AS 'Cube net puzzles'

Teacher's notes

Both the puzzles require pupils to visualise what happens to each square of a cube net when it is folded up to become a face of the cube. As they can check their solutions by actually folding up the nets, pupils will learn from their mistakes.

Solutions

1.

2.

3.

4.

5.

Nets with one continuous loop are: **A, C, D, G and H**.

Cube net puzzles

This cube has a black face on the top and a curved arrow on each of the four vertical faces. All the arrows point to the right.

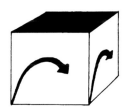

- Sketch each of these nets. Draw in the curved arrows so that each net will fold up to make the cube.

1.   **2.**   **3.**

4.   **5.**

Now cut out each net and fold it to see if you got it right.

- When some of these nets are folded to make a cube the black line makes one continuous loop.

  Which nets are they?

A.   **B.**   **C.**

D.   **E.**   **F.**

G.   **H.**   **I.**

- Sketch each net, cut it out and fold it to see if you are right.

Reflective symmetry

Learning objectives

◆ Sketch reflection in a mirror line where one or no point is touching.
◆ Sketch reflection in vertical, horizontal and sloping lines.
◆ Reflect a shape in a line not parallel to the sides of the shape.
◆ Recognise and explain patterns and relationships.

Resources

AS 'Black and white squares'

Teacher's notes

Pupils have to find reflections in four mirror lines.

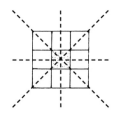

1. The other rings are:

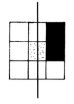 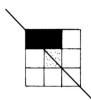

2. The rings are **different**.

3. The main challenge is to find an efficient system for checking all the possibilities. By following a good system pupils will know that they have checked all the possibilities. There are **12 different rings** with two black squares.

To get a set of 12 'different' rings, take one from each set of reflections of each of these.

Black and white squares

This is a ring of eight squares.

The squares can be black or white. If one ring can be reflected on to another, the rings are regarded as the **same**, otherwise they are **different**.

Example: is the **same** as 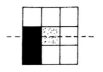 and

(Think where the mirror line is in each case.)

1. Draw all the other rings that are the **same** as:

2. Are these rings the **same** or **different**?
(If they are the **same**, sketch the mirror line.)

3. How many **different** rings are there with two black squares?
Try to be systematic and show your system.

Hint: going round the ring, the black squares can be together:

or 1 and 5 white squares apart: 　　or 2 and 4 white squares apart: 　　or 3 white squares apart:

Perimeter and area

Learning objectives

◆ Develop understanding of the terms 'perimeter' and 'area'.
◆ Solve mathematical problems or puzzles and make generalisations.

Resources

AS 'Same area, different perimeter'

Teacher's notes

Solutions

1. The area of both shapes given is **12cm²**. The perimeters are: **1.a. 20cm** and **1.b. 18cm**.

2. a. Possible perimeters are **14, 16, 18, 20, 22, 24 or 26cm**.

   b. 14cm is the smallest possible perimeter.

   c. 26cm is the greatest possible perimeter.

3. Possible perimeters for shapes with area 20cm² are: **18, 20, 22, 24, 26, 28, 30, 32, 34, 36, 38, 40, 42cm**.

Generalisations

● The possible perimeters are always even. This is because the shapes are all composed from rectangles. Whatever the shape, it can always be surrounded by a rectangle with the same perimeter.

Example:

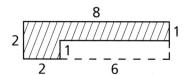
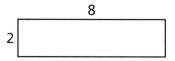

The perimeter of a rectangle has to be an even number because it is 2 x (length + breadth).

● The minimum perimeter is that of the most compact rectangle possible. The most compact rectangle is that closest to a square. For the area = 20cm², a 4cm by 5cm rectangle is the most compact.

● The maximum perimeter is that of the thinnest rectangle possible. For the area = 20cm², a 20cm by 1cm rectangle is the thinnest under the given conditions.

Same area, different perimeter

1. These two straight-sided shapes have the same area. What is it?

_____

What is the perimeter of each shape?

a. _____ **b.** _____

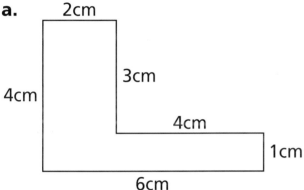

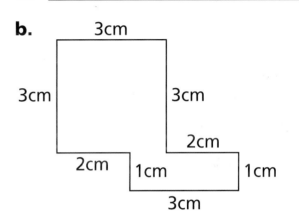

2. Sketch other straight-sided shapes with the same area as the shapes above, but with different perimeters. (Use whole number lengths for the sides and right-angles at the corners).

    a. What different perimeters are possible? _____

    b. What is the smallest possible perimeter? _____

    c. What is the greatest possible perimeter? _____

3. What different perimeters of straight-sided shapes with area 20cm² are possible? Sketch a shape with each possible perimeter. (Again use whole number lengths for the sides and right angles at the corners.)

_____

_____

Challenge
Write about anything general that you have discovered. Can you explain it?

Addition and subtraction

Learning objectives

◆ Use written procedures for addition and subtraction.
◆ Solve mathematical problems or puzzles and make generalisations.

Resources

AS 'Reverse – subtract – reverse – add'

Teacher's notes

This investigation requires perseverance and accuracy. It gives scope for generalisation from empirical findings (as opposed to reasoned argument). It requires perseverance because pupils may prematurely make wrong generalisations. For example, with three-digit numbers, the final number is always 1089.

Final numbers for the 'reverse – subtract – reverse – add' process.
        Two-digit numbers: 99.
        Three-digit numbers: 198 or 1089.
        Four-digit numbers: 1413 or 1998 or 9999 or 10 890.
        Five-digit numbers: 15 345 or 19 998 or 99 099 or 109 890.

Generalisation
The final numbers are multiples of 9. Most are also multiples of 11, but 1413 is not.

Name:	Date:

AS

Reverse – subtract – reverse – add

- Write any two-digit number, with the last digit smaller than the first, for example 73.

$$\begin{array}{r} 73 \\ -37 \\ \hline 36 \\ +63 \\ \hline 99 \end{array}$$

Reverse the digits and subtract.

Reverse the digits and add.

- Repeat this process for different two-digit numbers.
  What do you find?

- Write any three-digit number with the last digit smaller than the first, for example 854.

$$\begin{array}{r} 854 \\ -458 \\ \hline 396 \\ +693 \\ \hline 1089 \end{array}$$

Reverse the digits and subtract.

Reverse the digits and add.

- Repeat this process for different three-digit numbers.
  What do you find? (Do not jump to a hasty conclusion.)

- Do the same with four-digit numbers.
  What do you find?

- Do the same with five-digit numbers.
  What do you find?

- Look back at the special numbers that have appeared with two-digit, three-digit, four-digit and five-digit numbers.
  What is true about all these numbers?

_____

_____

© Folens (copiable page) Maths for the More Able 6 25

Properties of numbers and reasoning about numbers

Learning objectives

◆ Continue number sequences.
◆ Use a calculator to solve multi-step problems.

Resources

AS 'Cube-sum chains'
Calculators

Teacher's notes

By investigating these chains, pupils are likely to learn by heart the cubes of small numbers (for example, $2^3 = 8$, $3^3 = 27$, $4^3 = 64$, $5^3 = 125$).

Because they have to do calculations of the form $a^3 + b^3 + c^3$ many times, they will be motivated to use the calculator quickly and efficiently.

Short-cuts

● Once a number already in a chain is reached, no more calculating is necessary.

● Once a number (for example, 521) is in a chain, all the numbers that are rearrangements of the same digits (for example, 512, 125, 152, 215, 251) can also be placed because they all lead to the same next number.

This picture was built up starting from every number between 10 and 60. Other numbers, not in those chains, were placed using the short-cuts described above.

Cube-sum chains

This is how a cube-sum chain is made. You need to add the cubes of the individual digits to make another number.

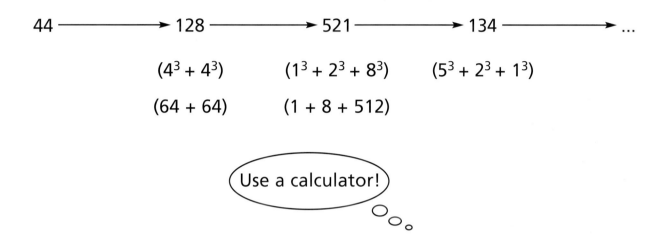

$44 \longrightarrow 128 \longrightarrow 521 \longrightarrow 134 \longrightarrow \ldots$

$(4^3 + 4^3)$ $(1^3 + 2^3 + 8^3)$ $(5^3 + 2^3 + 1^3)$

$(64 + 64)$ $(1 + 8 + 512)$

Use a calculator!

- Make chains from different starting numbers between 10 and 60. Can you find short-cuts?

- On a sheet of paper build up a picture of what happens. Which numbers are special? Why?

Place value, ordering and rounding

Learning objectives

◆ Divide by powers of 10 and understand the effect.
◆ Record answers using the appropriate units.
◆ Interpret information in a table.
◆ Round decimal fractions to the nearest tenth.

Resources

RS 'Zoom'
AS 'Our solar system'
Each pupil needs two large sheets of paper (at least A3 size)

Teacher's notes

Pupils have to think very carefully about the relationships between units (mm ➞ cm ➞ km). They also have to divide by very large powers of 10, round their answers and then measure accurately. Because the scale drawings should be very effective in conveying the reality of the dimensions of our solar system, pupils should be motivated to work accurately and see a reason for doing so.

1. The real radius of Neptune is divided by 1 000 000 000 **(1000 million)** to get the radius of the circle representing Neptune in the drawing. The radii of all the planets should be divided by 1000 million to get the radii of the circles in the drawing.

2.   **The radii of the circles**

Mercury	0.2439cm	**(2mm)**
Venus	0.6052cm	**(6mm)**
Earth	0.6378cm	**(6mm)**
Mars	0.3397cm	**(3mm)**
Jupiter	7.1492cm	**(71mm)**
Saturn	6.0268cm	**(60mm)**
Uranus	2.5559cm	**(26mm)**
Neptune	2.4764cm	**(25mm)**
Pluto	0.1160cm	**(1mm)**

3. Drawn to the same scale the radius of the Sun would be **69.5cm**. This would not fit on to an A3 sheet.

4. The single number that all the real distances are divided by is **250 thousand million** (250 000 000 000).

5. Using this scale, the radius of the Sun in the drawing is **0.0278mm**. This is far too small to draw, so the positions of the Sun and the planets will have to be represented by tiny dots.

Zoom

Our solar system

Name	Radius (km)	Average distance from Sun (1000km)
Sun	695 000	————
Mercury	2439	57 910
Venue	6052	108 200
Earth	6378	149 600
Mars	3397	227 940
Jupiter	71 492	778 330
Saturn	60 268	1 429 400
Uranus	25 559	2 870 990
Neptune	24 764	4 504 300
Pluto	1160	5 913 520

Our solar system

RS 'Zoom' has a chart showing the radius of the Sun and each planet in km and the average distance of each planet from the Sun in 1000km.

1. By what do you have to divide 24 764km (the radius of Neptune) to get 2.4764cm?

_____

On a large sheet of paper, draw Neptune as a circle with radius = 2.4764 (2.5cm to the nearest mm).

2. Find the radius of the circle for each planet drawn to the same scale as Neptune. Round the radius of each circle to the nearest mm. On the same sheet of paper, draw all the planets to this scale. It will give you a clear idea of the relative sizes of the planets.

3. What would be the radius of the Sun in a drawing using this scale? Would this fit on your large sheet of paper?

_____

● On the other sheet of paper you are going to make a scale drawing of the solar system, using a much smaller scale.

4. To find the distances in your scale drawing, divide all the real distances by 1 000 000 000 000 (one million million) then multiply by 4. (What single number will you have divided by?)

_____

5. a. Using this scale, what should be the radius of a drawing of the Sun?

_____

b. How will you represent the Sun and planets in this scale drawing?

_____

● Now do your scale drawing so that it gives a good idea of the relative distances of the planets from the Sun. You will have to make your own decisions about where to show the position of the Sun and the planets, but the distances must be correct.

FOLENS ICT FOR PRIMARY MATHS

"Delivering the essential ICT for your maths teaching"

Whatever Maths scheme you use, you are expected to use ICT within your Maths teaching.

Each pack comprises:

ONE CD-ROM PER YEAR containing:

- spreadsheets
- data useage
- roamer and logo work (shape, direction, angles, etc.)
- internet links
- multiple choice tests

ONE TEACHER FILE PER YEAR containing:

- lesson plans
- additional copiable activity sheets
- content linked to NNS

CD-Rom contains ready-made files for pupils to carry out work on spreadsheets and for handling roamer and logo work.

This pack provides the ICT you need for Primary Maths

From Age 8-9

From Age 8-9

ALSO AVAILABLE:

RAPID RECALL
10-minute tests of quick fire mental calculations for every year group.

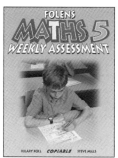

WEEKLY ASSESSMENT
A weekly, full record of achievement for every aspect of the Numeracy Strategy.

DEVELOPING NUMERACY
A comprehensive numeracy programme for teaching and assessing numeracy skills.

▼ PHOTOCOPIABLE ORDER FORM ▼

Please send me:

ICT FOR PRIMARY MATHS	RAPID RECALL	WEEKLY ASSESSMENT	DEVELOPING NUMERACY
☐ FB963X Age 5-6 Pack	☐ FA8168 Age 5-6	☐ FA8222 Age 5-6	☐ FA5819 Age 5-6
☐ FB9648 Age 6-7 Pack	☐ FA8176 Age 6-7	☐ FA8230 Age 6-7	☐ FA5827 Age 6-7
☐ FB9656 Age 7-8 Pack	☐ FA8184 Age 7-8	☐ FA8249 Age 7-8	☐ FA5835 Age 7-8
☐ FB9664 Age 8-9 Pack	☐ FA8192 Age 8-9	☐ FA8257 Age 8-9	☐ FA5843 Age 8-9
☐ FB9672 Age 9-10 Pack	☐ FA8206 Age 9-10	☐ FA8265 Age 9-10	☐ FA5851 Age 9-10
☐ FB9680 Age 10-11 Pack	☐ FA8214 Age 10-11	☐ FA8273 Age 10-11	☐ FA586X Age 10-11
ONLY £49.95 each. Price includes network licence	ONLY £14.95 each	ONLY £14.95 each	ONLY £14.95 each

Name:_____

School:_____

Address:_____

Postcode (vital): ☐☐☐☐☐☐☐

Tel:_____

Fax:_____

Signature:_____ 169

Order Hotline:	0870 6091235
Fax Orders:	0870 6091236
Customer Enquiries:	0870 6091237

Prices valid until 31/12/02

Post to: Folens Publishers Ltd, FREEPOST LOL1907, Boscombe Road, DUNSTABLE, Beds LU5 4RN

Understanding division

Learning objectives

◆ Give a quotient as a fraction or as a decimal when dividing by a whole number.
◆ Recognise and explain patterns and relationships, generalise and predict.
◆ Suggest extensions by asking 'What if ...?'.

Resources

AS 'Whole number part'

Teacher's notes

1.

$\left[\frac{5}{7}\right]$ $\left[\frac{10}{7}\right]$ $\left[\frac{15}{7}\right]$ $\left[\frac{20}{7}\right]$ $\left[\frac{25}{7}\right]$ $\left[\frac{30}{7}\right]$ $\left[\frac{35}{7}\right]$ $\left[\frac{40}{7}\right]$ $\left[\frac{45}{7}\right]$ $\left[\frac{50}{7}\right]$ $\left[\frac{55}{7}\right]$ $\left[\frac{60}{7}\right]$ $\left[\frac{65}{7}\right]$ $\left[\frac{70}{7}\right]$

0   1   2   2   3   4   5   5   6   7   7   8   9   10

2. Thinking about why a pattern appears will give pupils an opportunity to reason clearly and to try and explain that reasoning.

In each set of seven terms of the sequence of whole number parts, the first and second numbers are the same and the fourth and fifth numbers are the same (apart from the first set of six terms). This is because the remainders follow the repeating cycle:

$$0, \frac{5}{7}, \frac{3}{7}, \frac{1}{7}, \frac{6}{7}, \frac{4}{7}, \frac{2}{7}.$$

Adding $\frac{5}{7}$ to 0 (first remainder) or to $\frac{1}{7}$ (fourth remainder) does not 'arrive at' or 'go over' the next whole number. Therefore in each set of seven terms of the sequence, the whole numbers increase by five.

The seventh term is 5, therefore the fourteenth is 10, the twenty-first is 15 and so on. Any term of the sequence can be found by going back to the nearest position that is a multiple of seven, finding what the multiple is, then multiplying that number by five. You can then count on (taking account of repeats) to the position you want. For example, to find the number in the 145th position of the sequence, first go back to the nearest position that is a multiple of seven, the 140th. Because 140 = 7 x 20, multiply 20 by 5 to get the number in the 140th position (100). Starting from the 140th position the sequence is 100, 100, 101, 102, 102, 103, 104, 105, ... The number in the 145th position is 103.

3. The sequence $\left[\frac{4 \times n}{7}\right]$ again follows a pattern that is repeated every seven terms.

4. Pupils could investigate whether all sequences of the form $\left[\frac{a \times n}{7}\right]$ (with **a** being a whole number) follow similar patterns and try to explain why.

Pupils who really like to be challenged could then try to generalise further by trying different values for both a and b in $\left[\frac{a \times n}{b}\right]$.

Whole number part

Any number consists of a whole number part and a fractional part. The notation [ ] means **the whole number part**.

Examples:

$$[3.7] = 3 \qquad \left[6\tfrac{1}{4}\right] = 6 \qquad [7] = 7$$

The whole number part of 3.7 is 3 and the fractional part is 0.7 (or seven tenths).

The sequence $\left[\frac{5 \times n}{7}\right]$ produced by making n = 1, then n= 2, then n = 3 and so on starts:

$$\left[\tfrac{5}{7}\right] \qquad \left[\tfrac{10}{7}\right] \qquad \left[\tfrac{15}{7}\right] \qquad \left[\tfrac{20}{7}\right]$$

$$\left[\tfrac{5}{7}\right] \qquad \left[1\tfrac{3}{7}\right] \qquad \left[2\tfrac{1}{7}\right] \qquad \left[2\tfrac{6}{7}\right]$$

$$\quad 0 \qquad\quad 1 \qquad\quad 2 \qquad\quad 2$$

1. How do you think the sequence will continue?

2. Now continue working out the sequence until you can see a pattern. Try to explain the pattern.

3. What pattern does $\left[\frac{4 \times n}{7}\right]$ give?

● Investigate $\left[\frac{a \times n}{b}\right]$ with your own choice of a and b.

Example:

You could choose a = 2, b = 3 and investigate $\left[\frac{2 \times n}{3}\right]$
or
You could choose a = 5, b = 4 and investigate $\left[\frac{5 \times n}{4}\right]$

● In each case try to predict what the sequence will be. Then, when you have seen what it actually is, try to explain it.

Making decisions and checking results, including using a calculator

Learning objectives

- ◆ Decide on an appropriate way of calculating: mental, mental with jottings, written methods or calculator.
- ◆ Explain and record how a problem was solved.

Resources

AS 'Two discs'
Calculators

Teacher's notes

This is an opportunity for pupils to reason.

		4	**5**
To produce totals of 8, 9, 10, 11			
6 is on the back of 4, and 4 on the back of 5		6	4
or 3 is on the back of 4, and 7 on the back of 5		3	7
To produce totals of 6, 7, 8, 9		2	4
		3	3
To produce totals of 7, 8, 9, 10		2	6
		5	3
To produce totals of 9, 10, 11, 12		6	6
Possibilities for 3 consecutive totals			
7, 8, 9		3	4
8, 9, 10		3	6
9, 10, 11		5	6

This is also an opportunity for pupils to try to express their reasoning. For example, when finding ways of making three consecutive totals, pupils could use proof by contradiction as follows.

Nine has to be one of the totals, so the possible totals are 7, 8, 9 or 8, 9, 10 or 9, 10, 11.

Try 7, 8, 9: $\textbf{4} = a$ $\textbf{5} = b$

$4 + b = 7, 8$ or 9 so b is 3, 4, or 5.

If $b = 3$, $a = 5$ (to make $a + b = 8$) or $a = 3$ (to make $a + 5 = 8$). But if $a = 5$, totals are 7, 8, 9, 10 and if $a = 3$, totals are 6, 7, 8, 9.
So b cannot be 3.

If $b = 4$, $a = 2$ (to make $a + 5 = 7$) or $a = 3$ (to make $a + b = 7$). But if $a = 2$, totals include $6(a + b)$ and if $a = 3$, totals are 7, 8, 9.
So $b = 4$, $a = 3$, is a solution.

Two discs

Here are two discs.

A number is written on the front of each disc (4 and 5). There is also a number (not necessarily the same) written on the back of each disc.

- If I throw the discs in the air, then add the numbers on the faces when they land, I can produce the following four consecutive totals: 8, 9, 10, 11.

  Work out what numbers could be on the back of each disc.
  Is there more than one solution?

- Suppose I can produce a different set of four consecutive totals. Investigate the possible totals and the possible numbers on the back of each disc.

- Suppose I can produce only three different consecutive totals. What could be on the back of each disc?

Challenge
Explain how you reasoned this out.

Fractions and decimals

Learning objectives

- ◆ Convert a fraction to a decimal fraction.
- ◆ Convert a decimal fraction to a fraction.
- ◆ Explain methods and reasoning about numbers.
- ◆ Recognise and explain patterns and relationships, generalise and predict.

Resources

AS 'Top and bottom'

Teacher's notes

Solutions

$\frac{71}{101} = 0.70297$ which is **more than** 0.7.

$\frac{6}{7} = 0.857143$	$\frac{47}{100} = 0.47$	$\frac{2}{300} = 0.00\dot{6}$	$\frac{632}{850} = 0.743529$	$\frac{135}{140} = 0.964286$
$\frac{7}{8} = 0.875$	$\frac{48}{101} = 0.475248$	$\frac{3}{301} = 0.0099\dot{6}$	$\frac{633}{851} = 0.743831$	$\frac{136}{141} = 0.964539$

Adding 1 to both numerator and denominator of the fractions above increases the value of the fraction. Pupils are, therefore, likely to assume that this is always true. However, in all the fractions so far tried, the denominator is greater than the numerator (the fractions are all less than 1).
But the next example, $\frac{251}{245}$ is greater than 1 (the denominator is less than the numerator).

$$\frac{251}{245} = 1.02449 \qquad \frac{252}{246} = 1.02439$$

In this case adding 1 to both the numerator and denominator decreases the value of the fraction.

When the numerator is smaller than the denominator, 1 is a greater proportion of the numerator than of the denominator, so adding 1 to top and bottom increases the numerator by a greater proportion. The reverse is true if the numerator is greater than the denominator.

> If the fraction is less than 1, the value increases.
> If the fraction is equal to 1, the value stays at 1.
> If the fraction is greater than 1, the value decreases.

Subtracting 1 has the opposite effect. Adding or subtracting 10 to both numerator and denominator has the same effect, but to a greater degree.

Example: $\frac{15}{30} = 0.5$ $(+1) \longrightarrow \frac{16}{31} = 0.516129$ $(-1) \longrightarrow \frac{14}{29} = 0.482759$

       $(+10) \longrightarrow \frac{25}{40} = 0.625$ $(-10) \longrightarrow \frac{5}{20} = 0.25$

Top and bottom

$\frac{70}{100} = 0.7$

$\frac{71}{101} = \boxed{}$ Is it the same, or more, or less than 0.7?

- Try adding 1 to both the numerator and denominator of these fractions.

$$\frac{6}{7} \qquad \frac{47}{100} \qquad \frac{2}{300} \qquad \frac{632}{850} \qquad \frac{135}{140}$$

Try the same thing with other fractions.

Does adding 1 to both the numerator and denominator of any fraction always have the same effect?

- Try adding 1 to the numerator and denominator of this fraction.

$$\frac{251}{245}$$

Try the same thing with other fractions.

- What happens to the value of the fraction if you subtract 1 from both the numerator and denominator?

- How does the effect of adding or subtracting 10 to both the numerator and denominator compare with the effect of adding or subtracting 1?

Shape and space – position and direction

Learning objectives

- ◆ Read coordinates from a pair of axes.
- ◆ Interpret written questions.
- ◆ Recognise prime numbers and identify factors.
- ◆ Recognise and explain patterns and relationships and generalise.

Resources

AS 'Can you see it?'
Square dotted paper

Teacher's notes

The thinking required in this investigation will help with later work on gradients and equations of straight lines.

Every straight line through (0,0) and points on the grid has only one ring on it. As a result there are patterns in the horizontal and vertical rows.

Examples of patterns in rows and columns:

For x = 1 and y = 1 all the points are ringed.
For x = 2 and y = 2 every point is ringed.
For x = 3 and y = 3 the pattern is 2, space, 2 space, and so on.
For x = 4 and y = 4 every other point is ringed.
For x = 5 and y = 5 the pattern is 4, space, 4, space, and so on.

In the rows, the x-coordinates of the ringed points have no factors in common with the y-coordinate of the row. For example, in the row in which y = 2, the ringed points all have odd x-coordinates.

Similarly in the columns, the y-coordinates of the ringed points have no factors in common with the x-coordinate of the column. For example, in the column in which x = 6, only points with y-coordinates that are not multiples of two or three are ringed.

Generally, the coordinates of all ringed points are **relatively prime**; that is they have no factors, other than 1, in common.

Can you see it?

You need a sheet of square dotted paper.

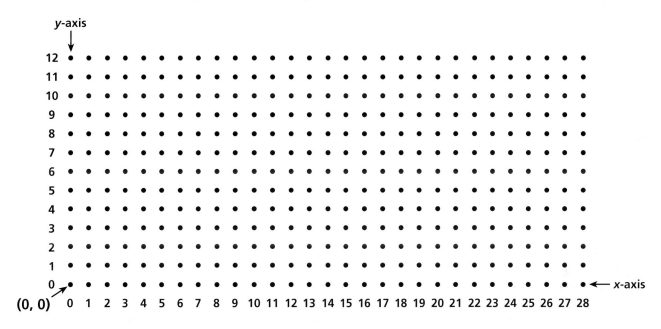

- Choose a point near the bottom left-hand corner of a sheet of square dotted paper.
  Mark the point (0,0).
  Mark the dots on the horizontal and vertical lines through (0,0):
  from 1 to 28 on the horizontal line and from 1 to 12 on the vertical line.

- Put a small ring around all the points on the grid that have no points directly between them and (0,0). You could imagine you are standing at (0,0). There is a tall post at each dot on the grid. You put a ring round only the posts that you can see. For example, you can see the post at (1,1) but the posts at (2,2), (3,3), (4,4) and so on are all hidden behind it. Try using a ruler to follow the line of sight.

- Look at the patterns of rings in each row and column.
  What has the pattern of rings got to do with the y-coordinate of the row or the x-coordinate of the column?
  Why do these patterns appear?

- Write the coordinates of the ringed points.
  What is generally true about the coordinates of these points?

Shape and space – position and direction

Learning objectives

◆ Know and use the term 'quadrilateral'.
◆ Use the properties of quadrilaterals.
◆ Understand and use the term 'perpendicular'.
◆ Recognise regular quadrilaterals.

Resources

AS 'Jigsaw'

Teacher's notes

This puzzle is not as easy as it might seem. It helps pupils focus on parallel, equal and perpendicular sides.

These are a few of the shapes that can be made.

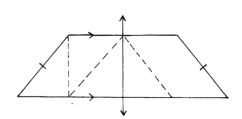

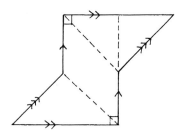

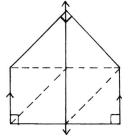

Isosceles trapezium
One pair of parallel sides.
One line of symmetry.
One pair of equal sides.

Irregular hexagon
Three pairs of parallel sides.
Two right angles.
Rotational symmetry.

Irregular pentagon
One pair of parallel sides.
Three right angles.
One line of symmetry.

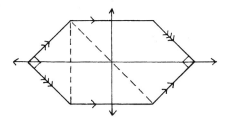

Irregular, but symmetrical hexagon
Three pairs of parallel sides.
Two right angles.
Two lines of symmetry.

Parallelogram
Two pairs of parallel sides.

Jigsaw

- Draw this rectangle carefully.

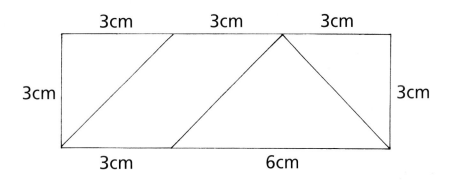

- Cut out the pieces.

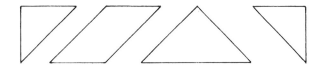

- Fit all four pieces together to make another shape.

Example:

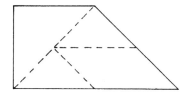

- What different quadrilaterals, pentagons, hexagons and so on are possible?

- What shapes with one, two or more sets of parallel sides are possible?

- What shapes with one, two or more right angles are possible?

- Sketch each shape, showing what you know about it.

Example:

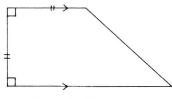

**Quadrilateral,
trapezium**
One pair of parallel sides.
Two right angles.

Length, mass and capacity

Learning objectives

- ◆ Know and use standard metric and imperial units for measuring capacity.
- ◆ Use conversions from metric to imperial units.
- ◆ Solve mathematical problems or puzzles.

Resources

AS 'Jugs'

Teacher's notes

If pupils are struggling, it may be helpful to show them part or all of the solution to one of the problems to give them the general idea of this kind of puzzle.

Solutions

1. Fill B.
  Fill A from B. This leaves 0.75 pints in B.
  Empty A. Pour the 0.75 pint from B into A.
  Fill B. Top up A from this. This leaves 1.5 pints in B.
  Empty A.
  Fill A from B. This leaves 0.5 pints in B as required.

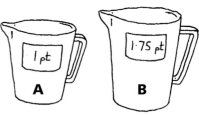

1 litre = 1.75 pints

1-pint jug   1.75-pint jug

A   B

2. Fill C, then empty it into D. Fill C and top up D from it.
  This leaves seven litres in C.
  Empty D. Pour the seven litres from C into D. Fill C.
  Top up D from C. This leaves five litres in C.
  Empty D. Pour the five litres from C into D. Fill C.
  Top up D from C. This leaves three litres in C.
  Empty D. Pour the three litres from C into D. Fill C.
  Top up D from C. This leaves one litre in C as required.

2 gallons = 9 litres

9-litre jug   11-litre jug

C   D

3. Fill F. Fill E from F. This leaves two litres in F.
  Empty E. Pour two litres from F into E.
  Fill F. Top up E from F. This leaves four litres in F as required.

7 pints = 4 litres

3-litre jug   5-litre jug

E   F

Jugs

1. You have a 1-litre jug (B) and a 1-pint jug (A), how can you use them to get a measured half pint in one of the jugs?

1 litre = 1.75 pints

1-pint jug   1-litre jug

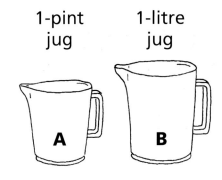

2. You have an 11-litre jug (D) and a 2-gallon (C) jug, how can you use them to get a measured 1 litre in one of the jugs?

2 gallons = 9 litres

2-gallon jug   11-litre jug

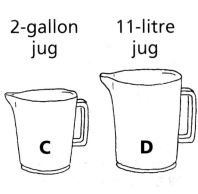

3. You have a 3-litre jug (E) and a 5-litre jug (F), how can you use them to get a measured 7 pints in one of the jugs?

7 pints = 4 litres

3-litre jug   5-litre jug

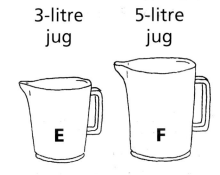

Challenge
Make up another problem like these about two jugs.
Work out the solution. Keep the solution to yourself and give your problem to someone (perhaps your teacher) to solve.

Handling data

Learning objectives

- ◆ Find the mean of a set of data.
- ◆ Interpret written problems.

Resources

AS 'Mean letters'

Teacher's notes

Pupils may need to be reminded of how to interpret a flow diagram. This investigation revises writing fractions greater than 1 as whole numbers with fractional parts. It also revises the spelling of words for numbers. Pupils should treat hyphenated words as separate (for example, twenty-eight is 6, 5).

What happens
All chains continue until 4 is reached.

Example:

three $\longrightarrow \dfrac{5}{1} = 5$

five $\longrightarrow \dfrac{4}{1} = 4 \longleftarrow$

four

Mean letters

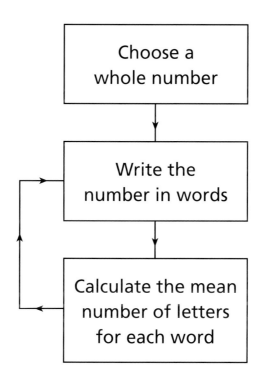

Example:

150

one hundred and fifty $\longrightarrow \dfrac{3 + 7 + 3 + 5}{4} = \dfrac{18}{4} = 4\frac{1}{2}$

$\longrightarrow$ four and a half $\longrightarrow \dfrac{4 + 3 + 1 + 4}{4} = \dfrac{12}{4} = 3$

three $\longrightarrow \dfrac{5}{1} = \dots$

and so on.

● Investigate this for different starting numbers.
  What happens?

Pencil and paper procedures – subtraction

Learning objectives

◆ Develop and refine written methods for subtraction.
◆ Subtract decimal fractions with up to four digits and up to two decimal places.
◆ Recognise and explain patterns and relationships, generalise and predict.

Resources

AS 'Shrinking squares and triangles'

Teacher's notes

Here are the completed shrinking squares given on the **AS**.

1.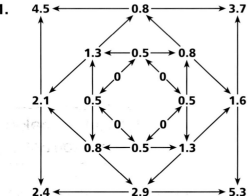

2.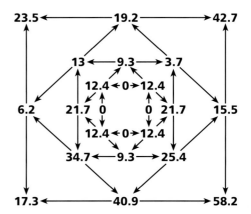

3.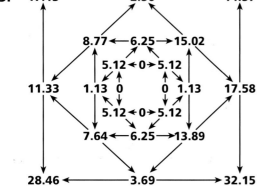

Generally, squares end with four noughts.

Triangles reach a set of three numbers of the form (x, x, 0), which repeats for ever.

Example: 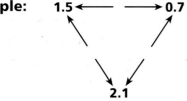 ends with (0.2, 0.2, 0)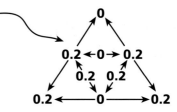

Shrinking squares and triangles

The number between two corner numbers is the difference between the two numbers.

● Copy and continue the 'shrinking squares'. What happens?

1.

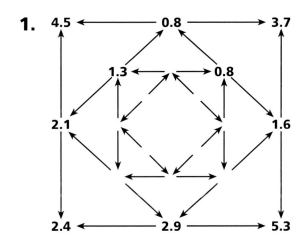

4.5 ← 0.8 → 3.7

1.3 ← 0.8

2.1 .... 1.6

2.4 ← 2.9 → 5.3

> Continue making new squares.

2.

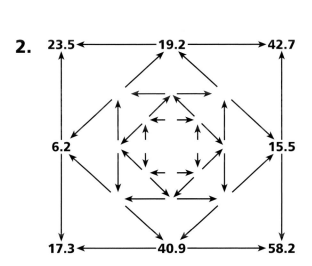

23.5 ← 19.2 → 42.7

6.2 .... 15.5

17.3 ← 40.9 → 58.2

3.

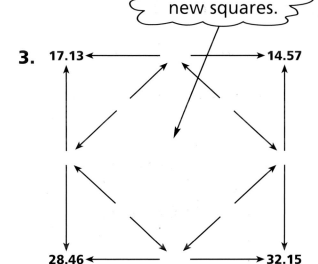

17.13 ← → 14.57

28.46 ← → 32.15

● Investigate 'shrinking squares', starting with your own choice of numbers at the four outside corners.
Include some four-digit starting numbers with two decimal places.
Does the same thing always happen?

● Investigate 'shrinking triangles'.
What happens?

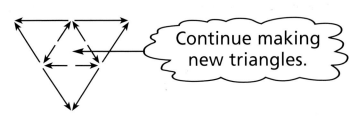

> Continue making new triangles.

Making decisions and checking results, including using a calculator

Learning objectives

◆ Choose appropriate number operations and appropriate ways of calculating to solve problems and puzzles.
◆ Explain and record how a problem was solved.

Resources

AS 'Bracelets'
Calculators

Teacher's notes

In sequences A, B, C and D each number is the sum of the two previous numbers. Sequences P, Q, R and S are obtained from sequences A to D respectively, by replacing numbers by the units digit only.

The rule produces cycles of numbers. Some cycles are long (the longest has 60 digits in it) and some are short. Because the cycles can be written as loops, 'bracelets' are a good description of them. Five different bracelets can be made.

Bracelets

● These sequences are all made using the same rule.
   What is the rule?

   A. 1, 4, 5, 9, 14, 23, 37, ...

   B. 2, 5, 7, 12, 19, 31, 50, ...

   C. 8, 3, 11, 14, 25, 39, 64, ...

   D. 13, 4, 17, 21, 38, 59, 97, ...

● How are these sequences (or chains) are derived from sequences A, B, C, D?

   P. 1, 4, 5, 9, 4, 3, 7, ...

   Q. 2, 5, 7, 2, 9, 1, 0, ...

   R. 8, 3, 1, 4, 5, 9, 4, ...

   S. 3, 4, 7, 1, 8, 9, 7, ...

● Choose any two starting digits and start a chain (sequence) yourself using
   the same system as for P, Q, R and S.
   Does it go on forever?

● Investigate what happens for other starting digits.
   Why is this investigation called 'Bracelets'?
   What bracelets can be made?

Properties of numbers

Learning objectives

◆ Recognise and use the terms 'multiple' and 'digit'.
◆ Recognise multiples.
◆ Solve mathematical problems or puzzles, generalise and predict.

Resources

AS 'Digit sums'

Teacher's notes

Multiples of 3 that are not also multiples of 9 produce cycles of 3, 6 and 9.

Starting numbers, such as 3, 12, 21, 30... give a digit sum beginning with 3.
The cycle is　⟶ 3 6 9 ⟶

Starting numbers, such as 6, 15, 24, 3... give a digit sum beginning with 6.
The cycle is　⟶ 6 3 9 ⟶

Numbers that have a digit sum of 1 (10, 19, 28, 37, 46, ...) produce the
cycle　⟶ 1 2 3 4 5 6 7 8 9 ⟶

Numbers that have a digit sum of 8 (8, 17, 26, 35, 44, ...) produce the
cycle　⟶ 8 7 6 5 4 3 2 1 9 ⟶

Other possible findings are summarised in the table.

Digit sum of starting number		Cycle produced by digit sums of multiples	
Sum to 9	1	⟶ 1 2 3 4 5 6 7 8 9 ⟶	Reverse of each other.
	8	⟶ 8 7 6 5 4 3 2 1 9 ⟶	
Sum to 9	2	⟶ 2 4 6 8 1 3 5 7 9 ⟶	Reverse of each other.
	7	⟶ 7 5 3 1 8 6 4 2 9 ⟶	
Sum to 9	3	⟶ 3 6 9 ⟶	Reverse of each other.
	6	⟶ 6 3 9 ⟶	
Sum to 9	4	⟶ 4 8 3 7 2 6 1 5 9 ⟶	Reverse of each other.
	5	⟶ 5 1 6 2 7 3 8 4 9 ⟶	
	9	⟶ 9 ⟶	

Digit sums

Choose any number, for example 14.

Start writing the sequence of multiples of the number.		Add the digits of each multiple to get the digit sum.	

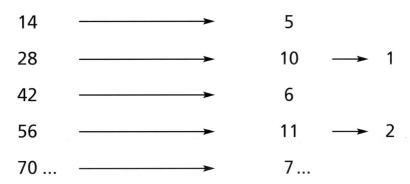

14	⟶	5	
28	⟶	10 ⟶ 1	
42	⟶	6	
56	⟶	11 ⟶ 2	
70 ...	⟶	7 ...	

Continue until you see the pattern made by the digit sums.

● Investigate the digit sums of multiples of other starting numbers.

● Which starting numbers give digit sums that are cycles of the numbers 3, 6 and 9?
Try to predict which other starting numbers will give digit sums following the same pattern.
Test your predictions.

● Which starting numbers give digit sums that follow this cycle?

┌→ 1 → 2 → 3 → 4 → 5 → 6 → 7 → 8 → 9 ┐

Predict other starting numbers that will give digit sums following this cycle.
Test your predictions.

● Which starting numbers give digit sums that follow this cycle?

┌→ 8 → 7 → 6 → 5 → 4 → 3 → 2 → 1 → 9 ┐

Predict other starting numbers that will produce this cycle.
Test your predictions.

● Write about the other things you discover.

Place value, ordering and rounding

Learning objectives

- ◆ Recognise and order negative and positive numbers.
- ◆ Find the difference between a negative number and either a positive or negative number.
- ◆ Solve mathematical problems or puzzles.
- ◆ Recognise and explain patterns and relationships, generalise and predict.

Resources

AS 'Number cells'
Squared paper

Teacher's notes

Solutions

1.a.

–2	–3	–5	–8	–13

b.

5	–8	–3	–11	–14

c.

–12	3	–9	–6	–15

2.a.

–5	1	–4	–3	–7

b.

–44	27	–17	10	–7

c.

–26	15	–11	4	–7

d.

–54	31	–23	8	–15

e.

–57	33	–24	9	–15

f.

–60	35	–25	10	–15

Investigation

3. a. If the number in the third cell is 0, the fourth number equals the fifth number.
   b. If the number in the second cell is 0, the fourth number is half the fifth number.
   c. If the number in the first cell is 0, the fourth number is two thirds of the fifth number.

4. a. When the fourth number increases by 1:
         the first number decreases by 3;
         the second number increases by 2;
         the third number decreases by 1.

   b. When the fourth number decreases by 1:
         the first number increases by 3;
         the second number decreases by 2;
         the third number increases by 1.

These findings can be explained algebraically, although this is not expected of pupils.
However, a few pupils may give explanations that are on the way to algebraic explanations.

Generally:

$2y - 3x$	$2x - y$	$y - x$	x	y

The first number decreases/increases by 3 because it is of the form $2y - 3x$ and $2y$ is constant.
The second number increases/decreases by 2 because it is of the form $2x - y$ and y is constant.
The third number decreases/increases by 1 because it is of the form $y - x$ and x is constant.

Number cells

You find the number in each cell by adding together the numbers in the two previous cells.

Example:

2	5	7	12	19

2 + 5   5 + 7   7 + 12

● Find the missing numbers.

1.a.

−2	−3			

b.

5	−8			

c.

−12	3			

● Find the missing numbers.

2.a.

			−3	−7

b.

			10	−7

c.

			4	−7

d.

			8	−15

e.

			9	−15

f.

			10	−15

Investigation

In this investigation you will need to draw your own sets of five cells – squared paper will help.

● Put any negative number in the fifth cell and then put any positive or negative number in the fourth cell.
Work out the other numbers.
Try this several times with different numbers.

3. What is the relationship between the fourth and fifth numbers if:
  a. the number in the third cell is 0?
  b. the number in the second cell is 0?
  c. the number in the first cell is 0?

   ● Try different numbers in the fourth cell, keeping the same number in the fifth cell.

4. a. What happens to the numbers in the first, second and third cells when the number in the fourth cell increases by one while the fifth number stays the same?
Try to explain why it happens.
  b. What happens when the fourth number decreases by one?
Try to explain what happens.

Understanding multiplication

Learning objectives

- ◆ Understand the operation of multiplication and its relationship to division.
- ◆ Use an appropriate strategy (mental, written or calculator) to solve written problems.
- ◆ Solve mathematical problems or puzzles.

Resources

AS 'Place the digits'
Calculators

Teacher's notes

Although the puzzles are about division statements, they are solved using multiplication and division.

The first puzzle is simply solved using multiplication as the inverse of division.
$(4 \times 5796 = 23\,184)$
      23 184 $\div 5796 = 4$

The second puzzle is easily solved if pupils remember that, if $a \div b = c$, then $a \div c = b$.
To find the missing number, simply divide 13 485 by 5. $(13\,485 \div 5 = 2697)$
      $13\,485 \div$ **2697** $= 5$

The remaining puzzles can be solved using trial multiplications (mental multiplication of one-digit numbers by one-digit numbers), known multiplication facts and reasoning. For example, the solution to the third puzzle can be worked out as follows.

      _ _ 1 _ 2 ÷ 5 _ _ _ = 6   This digit must be 2 or 7 to get 2 as the units digit when the number is multiplied by 6. However, 2 has already been used so it must be 7.

      _ _ 1_ 2 ÷ 5 _ _ 7 = 6

The digits left to choose from for this place are 3, 4, 6, 8 and 9. Try each digit in turn.

      3: _ _ 122 ÷ 5 _ 37   (not possible)   Four fits, but then, the digits 3, 6, 9 are
      4: _ _ 182 ÷ 5 _ 47   (not possible)   left to go in this place. However, none of
      6: _ _ 102 ÷ 5 _ 67   (not possible)   these gives 1 as the hundreds digit when
      8: _ _ 122 ÷ 5 _ 87   (not possible)   the number is multiplied by 6.
      9: _ _ 182 ÷ 5 _ 97   Therefore 9 is the tens digit here.

The digits left to choose from for the hundreds digit are 3, 4, 6. Try each in turn.

      3: 5397 x 6 = 32 382 (wrong)
      4: 5497 x 6 = 32 982 (wrong)
      6: 5697 x 6 = 34 182 (the solution!)

The solution is **34 182** $\div$ **5697 = 6**

The other solutions are: 4. 41 832 $\div$ **5976** $= 7$ **5. 25 496** $\div$ **3187** $= 8$ **6. 57 429** $\div$ **6381** $= 9$

Place the digits

In each division statement below a five-digit number is divided by a
four-digit number. Also, each of the nine digits 1, 2, 3, 4, 5, 6, 7, 8 and 9
appear once, and only once, to the left of the equals sign. 0 is not used.

● Fill in the missing digits to make the statements true.

1. __ __ __ __ __ ÷ 5 7 9 6 = 4

2. 1 3 4 8 5 ÷ __ __ __ __ = 5

3. __ __ 1 __ 2 ÷ 5 __ __ __ = 6

4. __ 1 __ 3 __ ÷ __ __ __ 6 = 7

5. 2 __ __ __ 6 ÷ __ 1 __ __ = 8

6. __ __ __ 2 __ ÷ __ __ 8 __ = 9

Making decisions and checking results, including using a calculator

Learning objectives

- Use the calculator's memory to complete calculations.
- Select the correct key sequence to carry out calculations involving more than one operation, including brackets.
- Explain methods and reasoning about numbers.
- Recognise and explain patterns and relationships, generalise and predict.

Resources

AS 'Fraction change'
Calculators

Teacher's notes

Any 'chain' made using a rule of the form:

$$\frac{\text{numerator}}{\text{denominator}} \longrightarrow \frac{(n \times \text{denominator}) - \text{numerator}}{\text{denominator} + (n \times \text{numerator})}$$

returns to the original fractions after two applications of the rule, where **n** is any whole number.

That is:　$$\frac{a}{b} \longrightarrow \frac{nb - a}{b + na} \longrightarrow \frac{n(b + na) - (nb - a)}{b + na + n(nb - a)} = \frac{a}{b}$$

because:　$$\frac{n(b + na) - (nb - a)}{b + na + n(nb - a)} = \frac{nb + n^2a - nb + a}{b + na + n^2b - na} = \frac{n^2a + a}{n^2b + b} = \frac{a(n^2 + 1)}{b(n^2 + 1)} = \frac{a}{b}$$

Although pupils are not yet expected to do this algebra.

By putting n = 1, some pupils may be able to understand what is happening. For example, n = 1, starting with $\frac{23}{61}$.

$$\frac{23}{61} \longrightarrow \frac{61 - 23}{61 + 23} \longrightarrow \frac{(61 + 23) - (61 - 23)}{(61 + 23) + (61 - 23)} = \frac{\cancel{61} + 23 - \cancel{61} + 23}{61 + \cancel{23} + 61 - \cancel{23}} = \frac{2 \times 23}{2 \times 61} = \frac{23}{61}$$

Pupils who get this far could be encouraged to replace the numbers with letters, to show the structure of what is happening.

Example:

$$\frac{a}{b} \longrightarrow \frac{b - a}{b + a} \longrightarrow \frac{(b + a) - (b - a)}{(b + a) + (b - a)} = \frac{\cancel{b} + a - \cancel{b} + a}{b + \cancel{a} + b - \cancel{a}} = \frac{2a}{2b} = \frac{a}{b}$$

In this way, almost without realising it, pupils move from a numerical demonstration towards an algebraic demonstration.

Fraction change

This is a rule for making a chain of fractions.

$$\frac{\text{numerator}}{\text{denominator}} \longrightarrow \frac{(33 \times \text{denominator}) - \text{numerator}}{\text{denominator} + (33 \times \text{numerator})}$$

Example:

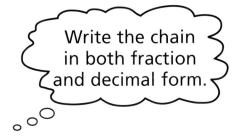

Write the chain in both fraction and decimal form.

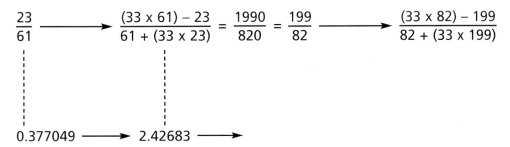

$$\frac{23}{61} \longrightarrow \frac{(33 \times 61) - 23}{61 + (33 \times 23)} = \frac{1990}{820} = \frac{199}{82} \longrightarrow \frac{(33 \times 82) - 199}{82 + (33 \times 199)}$$

$$0.377049 \longrightarrow 2.42683 \longrightarrow$$

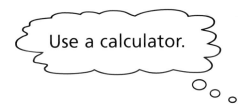

Use a calculator.

- Choose your own starting fraction with a two-digit numerator and a two digit denominator. What happens?

- Investigate chains from different starting fractions. What happens?

- What happens if you change the number 33 to another number?

- Can you explain why the chain behaves like this?
  Hint: try changing the 33 to 1.

Ratio and proportion

Learning objectives

◆ Solve simple problems involving ratio and proportion in context.
◆ Understand the difference between statements that compare part to part and those that compare a part to a whole.

Resources

AS 'Brickwork patterns'

Teacher's notes

For each wall pupils should write at least one statement that correctly gives the number of black (or white) bricks in every group of a certain number of bricks. To do this they will have to find a section of the pattern that repeats to make the whole pattern with no gaps. For example, in 2, this section of 9 bricks below repeats, in rows of 3 bricks, to make the whole pattern.

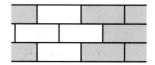

Pupils should also compare the number of black bricks with the number of white bricks in the whole wall (which is, of course, the ratio of black bricks to white bricks in the repeating section).

Solutions
1. 2 out of 3 bricks are black.   2 black for every 1 white.
   1 out of 3 bricks is white.

2. 5 out of 9 bricks are black.   5 black for every 4 white.
   4 out of 9 bricks are white.

3. 7 out of 16 bricks are black.   7 black for every 9 white.
   9 out of 16 bricks are white.

4. 1 out of 2 bricks is black.   Equal numbers of black and white.
   1 out of 2 bricks is white.

Brickwork patterns

Each diagram below shows part of a brick wall.

● For each wall write some statements about the proportion of the bricks that are black and the proportion that are white, also describing how the number of black bricks is related to the number of white bricks.

1. 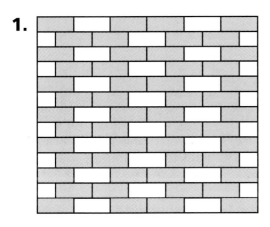 **2.**

3.  **4.**

● On this wall design your own pattern of black and white bricks. In your design, what proportion of the bricks are black and what proportions are white?
What is the ratio of black bricks to white bricks?

Percentages

Learning objectives

- Solve percentage problems without the use of a calculator.
- Recognise equivalence between percentages, fractions and decimals.
- Explain methods and reasoning about numbers.
- Recognise and explain patterns and relationships, generalise and predict.

Resources

AS 'Exploring percentages'

Teacher's notes

These investigations into the arithmetic of percentages are intended to give pupils a deeper understanding of percentages. Because pupils are asked to explain their findings, they need to think clearly of percentages as hundredth parts.

These investigations provide further practice in calculating percentages of numbers.

Percentage sums

     y% of A + y% of B = y% of (A + B)

This is an example of multiplication being distributive over addition.

Percentage differences

     y% of A – y% of B = y% of (A – B)

This is an example of multiplication being distributive over subtraction.

Percentage products

     y% of A x y% of B does **not** equal y% of (A x B)

But y% of A x y% of B = y% of y% of A x B

Example:
40% of 20 x 40% of 30 = 8 x 12 = 96
40% of 600 = 240 and 40% of 240 = 96

Percentages of percentages
Generally, y% of z% of A = $\frac{y \times z}{100}$ % of A

1. 20% of 20% of 50 = 2 = $\frac{400}{100}$ % of 50 = **4%** of 50

2. 20% of 50% of 30 = 3 = $\frac{1000}{100}$ % of 30 = **10%** of 30

3. 30% of 60% of 40 = 7.2 = $\frac{1800}{100}$ % of 40 = **18%** of 40

4. 20% of 90% of 70 = 12.6 = $\frac{1800}{100}$ % of 70 = **18%** of 70

Exploring percentages

- **Percentage sums**

  Work out: 20% of 50 + 20% of 60 and
  20% of 110.

  What do you find?

  Work out other percentage sums, such as: 15% of 40 + 15% of 90
  and   15% of 130.

  What is generally true?
  Try to explain why.

- **Percentage differences**

  Work out percentage differences, such as: 32% of 80 – 32% of 25
  and   32% of 55.

  What is generally true?
  Try to explain why.

- **Percentages products**

  Work out percentage products, such as: 40% of 20 x 40% of 30
  and   40% of 600.

  What do you find?
  Try to explain this.

- **Percentages of percentages**

  Find the missing percentages.

  1. 20% of 20% of 50 = _____% of 50

  2. 20% of 50% of 30 = _____% of 30

  3. 30% of 60% of 40 = _____% of 40

  4. 20% of 90% of 70 = _____% of 70

  Investigate other equations like these.

- Try to find a rule for writing a **percentage of a percentage** of a number
  as a **percentage** of the number. Can you explain why the rule works?

Handling data (1)

Learning objectives

◆ Know and recognise a simple pie chart.
◆ Interpret sections on a simple pie chart.
◆ Calculate values on a pie chart as a percentage.
◆ Explain methods and reasoning about numbers.

Resources

AS 'From one pie chart to another' (1)

Teacher's notes

These problems require pupils to extract information from pie charts and, linking the attributes differently, use it to construct further pie charts. They use ideas of proportion from earlier work. Pupils may find the results surprising.

The school choir
From the pie charts the following can be seen.

25% of 75% ($\frac{1}{4}$ of $\frac{3}{4}$) of the choir are girls in Y2 to Y4. So $\frac{3}{16}$ of the choir are girls in Y2 to Y4.

75% of 75% ($\frac{3}{4}$ of $\frac{3}{4}$) of the choir are girls in Y5 or Y6. So $\frac{9}{16}$ of the choir are girls in Y5 or Y6.

75% of 25% ($\frac{3}{4}$ of $\frac{1}{4}$) of the choir are boys in Y2 to Y4. So $\frac{3}{16}$ of the choir are boys in Y2 to Y4.

25% of 75% ($\frac{1}{4}$ of $\frac{1}{4}$) of the choir are boys in Y5 or Y6. So $\frac{1}{16}$ of the choir are boys in Y5 or Y6.

The proportion of the choir who are girls in Y2 to Y4 equals the proportion of the choir who are boys in Y2 to Y4. Therefore, of choir members in Y2 to Y4, half are boys and half are girls.

Choir members in Y2 to Y4

The proportion of the choir who are girls in Y5 or Y6 is $\frac{9}{16}$, while the proportion of the choir who are boys in Y5 or Y6 is $\frac{1}{16}$. Therefore, the ratio of girls to boys in Y5 or Y6 who are choir members is 9 to 1 (or $\frac{9}{10}$ are girls and $\frac{1}{10}$ are boys).

Choir members in Y5 or Y6

AS

From one pie chart to another (1)

In these problems you have to use the information in some pie charts to draw others.

The school choir
The pie chart shows the proportions of choir members who are boys and girls.

All choir members

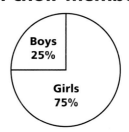

These pie charts show the proportions of the boys in the choir who are in Years 2–4 or Years 5 or 6, and the proportion of girls in the choir who are in Years 2–4 or Years 5 or 6.

Girls in choir   **Boys in choir**

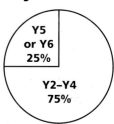

- Draw one pie chart to show the proportion of choir members in Years 2–4 who are boys and the proportion who are girls. Then draw another pie chart to show the proportion of choir members in Years 5 or 6 who are boys and the proportion who are girls.
  Write the fraction or percentage in each section.

Choir members in Y2–Y4

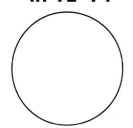

Choir members in Y5–Y6

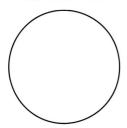

Handling data (2)

Learning objectives

◆ Know and recognise a simple pie chart.
◆ Interpret sections on a simple pie chart.
◆ Calculate values on a pie chart as a percentage.
◆ Explain methods and reasoning about numbers.

Resources

AS 'From one pie chart to another (2)'

Teacher's notes

These problems also require pupils to extract information from pie charts and, linking the attributes differently, use it to construct further pie charts.

Sandwich bar
The reasoning, which is similar to that for the school choir, leads to the following.

Prawn

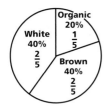

Chicken

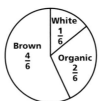

Egg

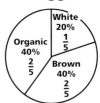

Organic: 25% of 25% ($\frac{1}{4}$ of $\frac{1}{4}$ = $\frac{1}{16}$).

Brown: 25% of 50% ($\frac{1}{4}$ of $\frac{1}{2}$ = $\frac{2}{16}$).

White: 50% of 25% ($\frac{1}{2}$ of $\frac{1}{4}$ = $\frac{2}{16}$).

The ratio of organic to brown to white = 1 to 2 to 2 ($\frac{1}{5}$, $\frac{2}{5}$, $\frac{2}{5}$).

Organic: 25% of 25% ($\frac{1}{16}$).

Brown: 50% of 50% ($\frac{4}{16}$).

White: 25% of 25% ($\frac{1}{16}$).

The ratio of organic to brown to white = 1 to 4 to 1 ($\frac{1}{6}$, $\frac{4}{6}$, $\frac{1}{6}$).

Organic: 50% of 25% ($\frac{2}{16}$).

Brown: 25% of 50% ($\frac{2}{16}$).

White: 25% of 25% ($\frac{1}{16}$).

The ratio of organic to brown to white = 2 to 2 to 1 ($\frac{2}{5}$, $\frac{2}{5}$, $\frac{1}{5}$).

From one pie chart to another (2)

Sandwich bar

These pie charts show the proportions of sandwiches made with different kinds of bread and the proportion of sandwiches made with each kind of bread with each type of filling.

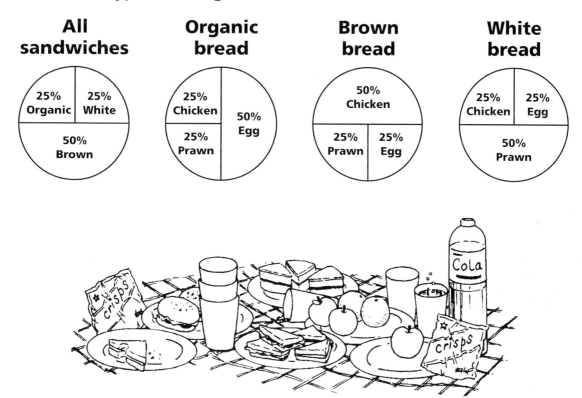

- Draw three pie charts.
  The first pie chart should show the proportions of prawn sandwiches made with organic, brown and white bread.
  The second should show the proportions of chicken sandwiches made with each kind of bread.
  The third should show the proportions of egg sandwiches made with each kind of bread.

  Write the fraction or percentage in each section.

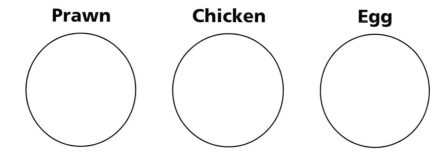

Using a calculator

Learning objectives

◆ Work through multi-step operation calculations.
◆ Use the memory key on a calculator.
◆ Solve mathematical problems or puzzles.

Resources

AS 'Targets'
Calculators

Teacher's notes

Encourage pupils to find as many different ways as possible to make target numbers from the numbers provided in the 'bubble'. There are numerous possibilities; some solutions are given here:

$$130 - [(74 + 15 + 1) \div 3] = 100$$
$$[(210 \times 3 + 15) \div (130 - 1)] \times (94 - 74) = 100$$

$$210 \div 3 - (94 - 74) = 50$$
$$130 - 74 - (15 \div 3 + 1) = 50$$

$$210 + 94 - (1 + 3) = 300$$

$$(94 - 74) \div (3 - 1) = 10$$

$$[(74 + 94 - (210 - 130)) \times 3] + 1 - 15 = 250$$

$$[130 - (210 \div 3) \div 15] + 94 + 1 = 99$$

Targets

- Make each target number using some or all of the numbers in the cloud and any of the following signs: +, −, ÷, x, (,), [,].

  When trying to make a target number, you can only use each number once, but you can use each of the signs and brackets as many times as you like.

  Some of the targets can be made in several different ways.

  How many of them can you find?

Numbers

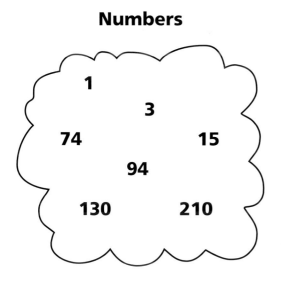

Target

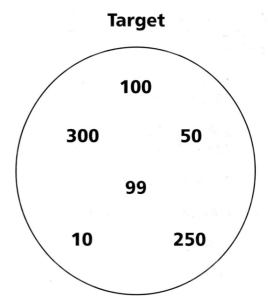

Shape and space – angle

Learning objectives

◆ Work confidently with measuring and drawing angles.
◆ Use the vocabulary of angles appropriately.
◆ Know that the angle of a straight line is 180°.
◆ Solve mathematical puzzles involving shapes, recognise and explain patterns and relationships, generalise and predict.

Resources

AS 'Doodle-stars'
Rulers

Teacher's notes

- The angles at the points of any 'doodle-star' add up to 180°.

Explanation

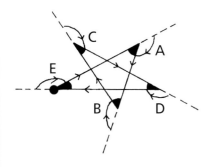

If you travel around the 'doodle-star' from the point marked •
in the direction of the arrows, the total angle turned through
is $\hat{A} + \hat{B} + \hat{C} + \hat{D} + \hat{E}$.

The total angle turned through is also 2 x 360° because you
end up facing in the same direction as when you set off, and
you also face that direction during one of the turns en route;
that is you do two full turns.

So $\hat{A} + \hat{B} + \hat{C} + \hat{D} + \hat{E}$ = 2 x 360° = 4 x 180°.

But each angle at a point, together with one of the angles
$\hat{A} + \hat{B} + \hat{C} + \hat{D}$ or $\hat{E}$ makes 180° (straight line). There are five
such pairs. So, the sum of the angles at the points is
$\hat{A} + \hat{B} + \hat{C} + \hat{D} + \hat{E}$ = 5 x 180°.

Therefore, the sum of the five angles at the points is
5 x 180° – 4 x 180° = 180°.

- Each angle at a point of a regular 'doodle-star' = 180° ÷ 5 = 36°.
  The five straight lines of a regular 'doodle-star' are equal in length.
  A regular 'doodle-star' has five lines of symmetry.

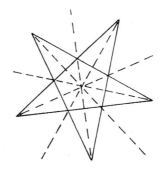

Doodle-stars

This is how to draw a doodle-star.
You draw five straight lines, making five points and end up where you started.

A doodle-star
has five points.

 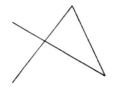  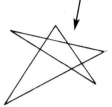

Here are some doodle-stars.

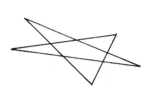 

- Draw your own doodle-stars.

Use a ruler!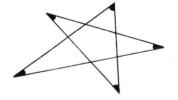

Measure the angles at each point.
Add up these angles.
What do you find?

- Draw some different doodle-stars.
On each doodle-star, measure and add up the angles at each point.
What do you find?

Try to explain your findings.
(**Hint**: imagine going around a doodle-star on its lines. Think about the total angle you have turned through by the time you get back to where you started from. Now think about angles on a straight line.)

- If the angles at the points of a doodle-star are all equal, what is the angle?

- Draw a doodle-star in which the angles at the points are all equal (a regular doodle-star).
What else is true about a regular doodle-star?
(**Hint**: making a guess about this may help you draw one!)

Shape and space – angle

Learning objectives

- ◆ Measure and draw bearings.
- ◆ Use angles and bearings in context.
- ◆ Recognise and explain patterns and relationships.

Resources

AS 'A rock and a tree'
RS 'A rock and a tree'

Teacher's notes

The difference between the greater bearing and the smaller bearing must be 180°, whatever the relative positions of the rock and the tree. Pupils ought to be able to explain why this is true, using the fact that angles on a straight line add up to 180°.

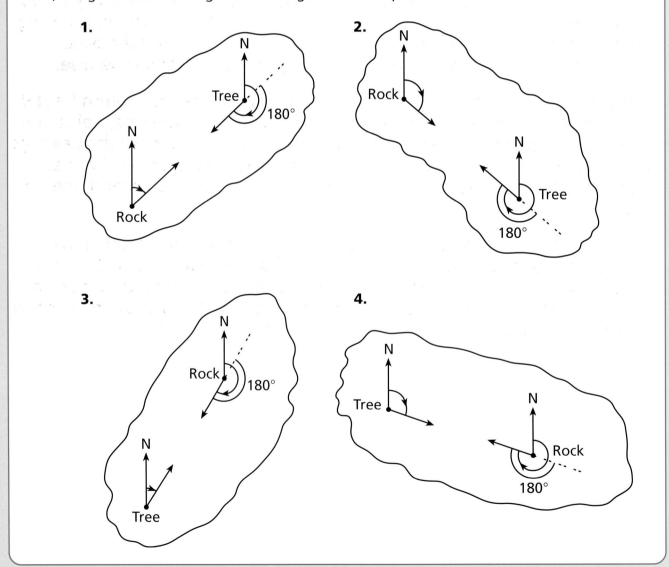

A rock and a tree

Raj strode off early one morning for a walk on the moor. He was so deep in thought that he took little notice of the direction in which he headed. But on he walked, mile after mile, until it was quite late and he began to feel tired.

Seeing a rock nearby, he climbed on to it for a rest. As the young man gazed absent-mindedly about him, he began to realise that he was completely lost. Even worse was the realisation that the only landmark he could see was a lonely tree in the distance.

Fortunately Raj knew how to use his watch and the sun's direction to get a bearing of the tree. Having made a mental note of the bearing of the tree from the rock, he jumped down and set off in the direction of the tree.

When he reached the tree Raj scrambled up on to a big branch and looked out over the moor. To his horror, all that was visible, other than the bleak grass, was the rock on which he had rested a while earlier. His unease was starting to turn to fear. Without thinking how it could help him, the exhausted walker used his watch again to get a bearing of the rock from the tree.

Having in his mind both the bearing of the tree from the rock, which he still remembered, and now also the bearing of the rock from the tree, Raj sat on the branch for some time wondering what he could deduce from the bearings. Eventually, he concluded that this knowledge was useless. So he chose at random a direction in which to go, hoping that soon he would find himself in familiar surroundings.

Raj climbed down from the tree. As he tramped off wearily towards the horizon, he thought about the two bearings he had taken. He realised that they were connected in an interesting way. By the time he reached the track that would lead him home, Raj had worked out why they were connected in this way, and his long walk felt worthwhile after all.

A rock and a tree

● In what way was the bearing of the tree from the rock connected to the bearing of the rock from the tree?
Explain why.

Hints

Mark two points on the page, one for the rock and the other for the tree.
Measure the bearing of the tree from the rock, then the bearing of the rock from the tree.
Repeat with the tree and the rock in other relative positions.

Examples:

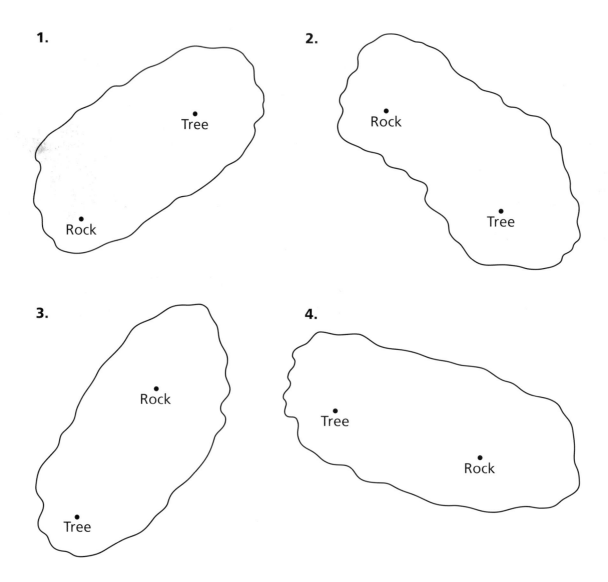

Maths for the More Able 6

© Folens (copiable page)

A Spanish floor

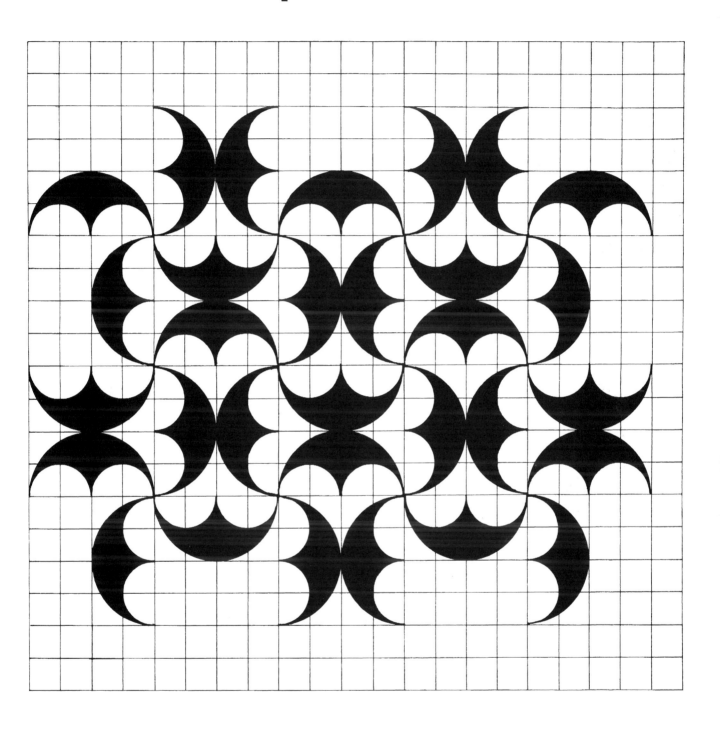

Shape and space – rotation

Learning objectives

◆ Use 90° and 180° rotations.
◆ Draw shapes after they have rotated 90° or 180° around a vertex.

Resources

AS 'A Spanish floor'
Squared paper
Compasses

Teacher's notes

The illustration on page 73 shows the result that should be achieved by pupils following the instructions on the **AS** 'A Spanish floor'.

Pupils will need squared paper and compasses for this activity. For a good result, they need to start their designs near the centre of the page of squared paper. Encourage them to be careful and accurate in their drawing.

A Spanish floor

There is a beautiful Roman mosaic pattern on the floor of a courtyard in a museum in Cordoba in southern Spain. Follow these instructions to reproduce the design.

You need squared paper and a compass.

- First draw this shape made from three semi-circles, somewhere near the centre of your page.

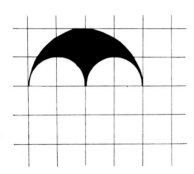

Think where the centres of the semi-circles are.

- Rotate the shape 90° about its left-hand 'point', and draw it again. Rotate it a further 90° about the same 'point' and draw it again. Rotate it a further 90° about the same 'point' and draw it in the fourth position.

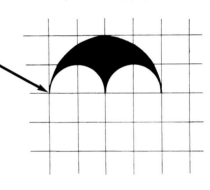

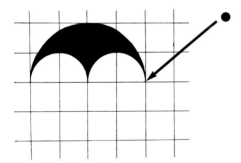

- Now rotate the original shape 90° about its right-hand 'point'. Keep rotating the shape 90° about the same 'point' and draw it after each rotation.

- Now transfer your attention to any one of the new copies of the shape, either horizontal ⌣ or vertical 🌙.

Make new copies of the shape by rotating it about whichever of its two 'points' has not so far been a centre of rotation.
Continue making new copies of the shape in this way until your whole page is filled.

Making decisions and checking results

Learning objectives

> ◆ Develop calculator skills and use a calculator effectively.
> ◆ Use a calculator to solve problems.
> ◆ Solve mathematical puzzles, recognise and explain patterns and relationships, generalise and predict.

Resources

> **AS** 'Av-beast'
> Calculators

Teacher's notes

> The challenge in these problems is to know what calculations to do. Pupils have to realise (or work out) that to find the new number, that has to be added to those already there to change the average, they have to find the difference between the product of the number of numbers already there and the present average, and the product of the new number of numbers and the required average.
> That is:
>
> $$\text{new number} = (\text{new number on 'counter'} \times \text{new average}) - (\text{old number on 'counter'} \times \text{old average}).$$
>
> This investigation should also lead to generalisations.
>
> ● The numbers that need to be eaten by the 'av-beast' to increase the average by 1 each time from the initial average of 62.47 are: 79.47, 81.47, 83.47, and so on.
>   These numbers increase by 2.
>
> ● To increase the average by 0.1 each time from the initial average of 2.8, the 'av-beast' must eat the following sequence of numbers: 3.9, 4.1, 4.3, 4.5, and so on.
>   These numbers increase by 0.2.
>
> ● The numbers that the 'av-beast' must eat to increase the average by 0.01 each time from the initial average of 0.23 are: 0.51, 0.53, 0.55, and so on.
>   These numbers increase by 0.02.
>
> Generally, if the average of a set of numbers continually increase by 10^n, the new numbers that have to be included in the set of numbers increase by 2×10^n.

Av-beast

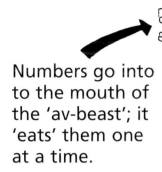

Numbers go into to the mouth of the 'av-beast'; it 'eats' them one at a time.

The 'av-beast' calculates the average of the numbers inside it and displays the average on a big screen.

The counter on its neck shows how many numbers the 'av-beast' has eaten.

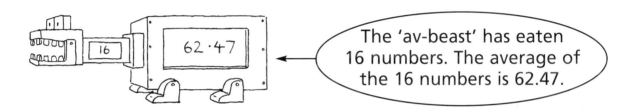

The 'av-beast' has eaten 16 numbers. The average of the 16 numbers is 62.47.

- What number should the 'av-beast' eat next to make the average increase by 1 to 63.47?
  What number should it then eat to make the average again increase by 1 to 64.47?
  Investigate the numbers it should continue to eat so that, as it eats them one at a time, the average continues to increase by 1 each time?

- Investigate the sequence of numbers the 'av-beast' should continue to eat so that, as it eats them one at a time, the average increases by 0.1 each time to 2.9, and then to ...

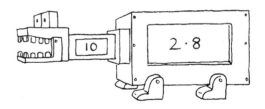

- Investigate the sequence of numbers the 'av-beast' should continue to eat so that, as it eats them one at a time, the average increases by 0.01 each time to 0.24, and then to ...

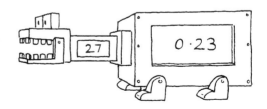

- What have you found to be generally true?
  Write about your findings.

Properties of numbers

Learning objectives

◆ Know prime numbers to at least 20.
◆ Recognise prime numbers to 100.
◆ Solve mathematical puzzles, recognise and explain patterns and relationships, generalise and predict.

Resources

AS 'Primes and squares'

Teacher's notes

Prime numbers that are the sum of two squares	Prime numbers that are not
$2 = 1^2 + 1^2$	3
$5 = 1^2 + 2^2$	7
	11
$13 = 2^2 + 3^2$	
$17 = 1^2 + 4^2$	19
	23
$29 = 2^2 + 5^2$	31
$37 = 1^2 + 6^2$	
$41 = 4^2 + 5^2$	47
$53 = 2^2 + 7^2$	59
$61 = 5^2 + 6^2$	67
	71
$73 = 3^2 + 8^2$	79
	83
$89 = 5^2 + 8^2$	
$97 = 4^2 + 9^2$	

A prime number is the sum of two squares if it is 1 more than a multiple of 4 (excluding 2). So if, when you subtract 1 from the prime number, you reach a multiple of 4, the prime number is the sum of two squares.

Primes and squares

The seventeenth-century French mathematician, Fermat, discovered that exactly half the prime numbers are the sum of two squares.

Example: $41 = 4^2 + 5^2$ ($41 = 16 + 25$)

● Investigate the prime numbers less than 100. Make one list of the prime numbers that are the sum of two squares and another list of those that are not.

● Try to find a rule that tests whether or not a prime number is the sum of two squares.
  Hint: the number 4 has something to do with it.

United Kingdom: Folens Publishers, Apex Business Centre, Boscombe Road, Dunstable, LU5 4RL.
Email: folens@folens.com

Ireland: Folens Publishers, Greenhills Road, Tallaght, Dublin 24.
Email: info@folens.ie

Poland: JUKA, ul. Renesansowa 38, Warsaw 01–905.

Editor: Katherine Seddon
Layout artist: Jane Conway
Illustrations: Kirsty Wilson and Liz McIntosh of Graham-Cameron Illustration
Cover design: Martin Cross

First published in 2001 by Folens Limited.
Reprinted 2002.

British Library Cataloguing in Publication Data. A catalogue record for this publication is available from the British Library.

ISBN 1 84163 941–9